mac's year
1986

Cartoons from the Daily Mail

Stan McMurtry mac

**Published by Associated Magazines Ltd for
Mail Newspapers p.l.c.
London EC4Y 0JA**

© Stan McMurtry 1986

ISBN 0 85144 362 1

Printed in Great Britain by
Spottiswoode Ballantyne Ltd., Colchester and London.

AUGUST 13

'We're getting there, Maggie. If we keep up the H.P. payments, in three years we should own both Mr MacGregor's legs, an arm and a bit of his nose.'

'The commuters have decided a "passengers only" service is more efficient.'

AN 'UNCHRISTIAN' traffic warden took the number of a hearse and mourners' cars parked outside a church for a funeral — and has been rebuked by a vicar from the pulpit. Police were called in

AUGUST 16

'Oh, yes? — and whose funeral is it this time?'

'Right! There'll be no more near misses! — left hand down a bit . . . not too fast . . . mind those birds . . . !'

AUGUST 19

'Now, come along! How on earth are we ever going to take over as doctors if you keep writing perfectly legible prescriptions?'

'Mummy's following behind — she has the tickets.'

AUGUST 21

'That's true, Mrs Petrinski. I did ask you to dust my office . . . however . . .'

'OK, Louie, if you spill the beans I can't promise you'll be made President, but we'll do our best.'

'Remember, mes amis. The new kit will be worn on all future overseas assignments . . . !'

'Jimmy? — that's a nice name. You're new here aren't you?'

SEPTEMBER 2

'Look out! — It's Rambo Maxwell!'

SEPTEMBER 3

'It's about the reshuffle, Mr Thatcher, Sir — I'm afraid I've got some rather bad news . . .'

'Ah, Leon. — As a start to my crackdown on crime, I wonder if you could help with my inquiries?'

SEPTEMBER 4

'Hello, David dear — I heard a rumour that there's a teensy-weensy rift between you and your friend Steel . . .'

mac

Now he's gone to Russia again

ARTHUR SCARGILL was in Russia—again—yesterday. He was arranging the inaugural meeting of the East-West Miners' Trade Unions International which will be held in Paris in two weeks.

The International is his idea but many of his opponents fear that it will be a Soviet-dominated facade.

HALT
SIBERIAN
LABOUR CAM

SEPTEMBER 10

'There seems to have been some mistake! — I'm here to form a new miners' international organisation with me as President.'

SEPTEMBER 11

'Naturally, we shall be appealing to the High Court over these £4,000 fines — meanwhile, the tunnel under the bank is progressing satisfactorily . . .'

'I don't know whether you chaps are in the mood, but I'm longing for . . . a nice cup of tea.'

SEPTEMBER 18

'I know you want it to be a surprise for the P.M., Sir, but I'm sure she'd appreciate a quick phone call before you annihilate Liverpool.'

'He was just passing by and wondered if we'd like to come to a great party down at the fire station.'

mac

NURSERY SCHOOL

WITH an irrepressible wink that might well signal much mischief-making to come in class, Prince William returned home from holiday at Balmoral yesterday to the news that today he's starting school.

SEPTEMBER 25

'Remember now, low and husky . . . "Hi William, I'm Hermione and free from all social engagements at the moment . . ."'

'Look, Neil — I know you're keen to project this new authoritative leader image, but . . .'

OCTOBER 1

'Well, when can he start school again? I'm worried that if he misses any more lessons his writing and grammar will suffer.'

'You'll have to wait — the fines will be paid by the Labour Party after the next election.'

OCTOBER 4

'With a bit of luck, when they shake hands, he'll think it's that lightning bolt of love he's been on about.'

'Icky bicky, guggle flugabub, boo gurgle . . .'

OCTOBER 9

'I can't understand it — all I ever get are nice young men who have strangled, cut up and boiled their wives.'

'What with Prince Andrew meeting Selina Scott, Anne meeting Wogan and now the Di and Charles show, I think someone is feeling a bit left out . . .'

'Okay, tuck this lot up in jail, officer — we'll be back with some more in half an hour.'

OCTOBER 22

OCTOBER 23

'Okay – lights, camera ... action!'

OCTOBER 25

'I know how you feel, Charles, but couldn't we retain just one teensy weensy little no-go area?'

'Now, remember, when the Government inquiry team comes over here, I want no mention of the rack.'

'Don't worry — it's probably a recruitment drive by the Workers' Revolutionary Party.'

'Nice place you've got here, squire. We'd hate to see a tempest, pestilence or a plague of locusts come in if the doors were open on a Sunday . . .'

'A free holiday in France with £5 to spend — I knew there'd be a catch!'

'... Once again, Princess Diana has insulted the Australian people by turning out in another incredibly shoddy ...'

'Please! We were only two minutes overdue!'

NOVEMBER 18

'Another man of peace from Northern Ireland — wants to know what you'll be doing with all the missiles you're thinking of scrapping.'

NOVEMBER 19

'Relax — we're only here to stop any bloodshed or violence from outside.'

'Is it important?'

NOVEMBER 26

'United Arab Hijackers and Lunatics Association? — That'll do nicely, Sir.'

'I thank the accused for his note, but telling me I've got lovely eyes and a nice smile won't make the slightest difference to the sentence he's about to get . . .'

'For years, the Church laboured on this report, brethren, but does anyone listen?'

DECEMBER 3

'Do you think anyone will notice?'

THE Prince and Princess Michael of Kent walked off a plane at Heathrow yesterday after being besieged by Press cameramen.

Their flight to Rome for a private audience with the Pope was grounded until the photographers surrendered their equipment.

DECEMBER 9

'Your Holiness — I fear that there has been a grave mistake . . .'

mac

LABOUR was accused yesterday of trying to kill off the fixed Channel link by insisting on a long drawn-out public inquiry.

Transport Secretary Nicholas Ridley, who wants to speed things up by leaving the decision to Parliament warned that an inquiry would sound the project's 'death knell'.

As MPs began a major debate on the plan Mr Ridley insisted that the only way to ensure a rapid decision was through an all-party parliamentary select committee which, he promised, would hear evidence from objectors.

DECEMBER 10

'. . .and, in the Commons, the Prime Minister emphatically denied that there was any unseemly rush to start the Channel link . . .'

DECEMBER 11

'Looks like that Ian Botham guy finally made it in Hollywood.'

'Sir, remember saying "Let's hope we've seen an end to the Defence Secretary's astonishing and distasteful tactics."'

DECEMBER 18

'You fool! Parking on a double yellow line. I told you there might be a Leon Brittan bodyguard about.'

ACTRESS Charlotte Cornwell, who was savaged by a newspaper's TV critic, won £10,000 libel damages yesterday.

The former Rock Follies star sued the Sunday People after Nina Myskow wrote: 'Her bum's too big' and 'she has the sort of stage presence which jams lavatories.'

She made the flame-haired actress her 'Wally of the Week' for h...

DECEMBER 20

'Remember your comments about the angel's performance in the nativity play, dear? Well, he's suing you for £10,000.'

'Did you remember to leave a Christmas box for the dustmen?'

DECEMBER 23

DECEMBER 24

'The dear old girl from your office that you bought a shawl for says it doesn't fit and will you change it after Christmas?'

mac

IT WAS at a Cabinet committee on December 9 that Margaret Thatcher's suspicion first broke surface that she might be involved in a poker game where the stakes could ultimately involve her own leadership.

On the agenda was another of those time-consuming relatively minor issues that torment and distract every Government from its broad brush approach to rule: the future of Westland helicopters.

Exasperated by the thinly-veiled personality quarrel that had been going on between two Ministers, Mrs Thatcher drew the discussion to a close in brusque fashion

JANUARY 3

'. . . and what about you, Leon? Have you made any jolly New Year resolutions?'

MICHAEL HESELTINE quit the Cabinet yesterday in a naked challenge to the way Margaret Thatcher runs the Government, the Tory Party and the country.

He resigned ...iquely, by walking ...

WESTLAND

JANUARY 10

'There has been a sharp increase in the number of unemployed.'

JANUARY 13

'I think it's to scotch any rumours that she's quitting.'

'Muammar — are you expecting visitors?'

JANUARY 15

'It's the same every morning! A bloke with long hair and a loin-cloth swoops down, rifles through the letters, then disappears!'

JANUARY 17

'I do wish Heseltine wouldn't be quite so dramatic.'

THE Royal Yacht Britannia was forced to pull out of South Yemen yesterday, leaving dozens of Britons stranded amid shellfire and worsening civil war.

It happened when beaches packed with hundreds of fleeing foreigners came under heavy fire.

Some waded chest deep into the sea to haul themselves into the last of the small boats sent from Britannia before she slipped anchor.

JANUARY 20

'I don't care if your clothes got ruined getting off the beach — put these back in the wardrobe where you found them!'

'. . . so that's a nice bit of Camembert for tea, a few bottles of Chablis and don't forget the Gauloises fags for mother . . .'

Maggie won't deny Greenham spy claim

MRS THATCHER yesterday refused to deny reports that Russian women agents had infiltrated the Greenham Common protesters.

JANUARY 22

'Can you spare a moment, Olga? The girls would like to talk to you about these rumours.'

'I warn the Prime Minister. There are a lot more facts about Westland that the public are desperately anxious to learn.'

JANUARY 24

'Don't bother, Hopkins, my wife informs me that *The Times* has been delivered as normal this morning.'

FEBRUARY 3

'You were supposed to swap Shcharansky for one of our spies, Oleg!'

'Ladies, have you tried tingling fresh H_2O from the Zippy Water Corporation?'

'We couldn't think what to do about yobbos with chemicals, then we got a call from Percy Thrower . . .'

FEBRUARY 14

'We'll shoot the love scene just once more, Harold — but this time without the pipe . . .'

FEBRUARY 17

'Aw, c'mon, Samantha! Forget how difficult it was getting past the pickets — try and look a bit more sexy!'

FEBRUARY 18

'Never mind the opinion polls, I'm staying.' . . . 'Atta girl! Atta girl!'

mac

PRINCESS ANNE is to ride as an amateur jockey in the coming flat race season, Buckingham Palace said yesterday.

This effectively ends rumours that she is expecting her third child in the summer.

FEBRUARY 19

'Amateur jockey or not, I still think there might be some truth in the rumours.'

FEBRUARY 21

'Are you lonely, Dearie? — oops, sorry, M'lud!'

THE QUEEN was hit by an egg hurled by a teenage girl demonstrator today on the first full day of her New Zealand tour.

It hit her on the hip, smearing her pink wool coat. A second

FEBRUARY 25

'Thank you, Perkins, that will be all — I think we're ready for them tomorrow.'

'I hope you won't mind sharing — we're expecting the Liverpool tyrant Derek Hatton and his henchmen any day now.'

'Well, really! Sometimes, I think Ted Heath goes too far!'

EDWARD HEATH dealt a triple snub to Margaret Thatcher as Tory leader yesterday.

Three times in a TV interview he was invited to endorse her to lead the party into the next election.

Three times he refused.

MARCH 4

'You'll take it, Mr Hatton? — good. Now I expect you'll want to know about the rates . . .'

MARCH 10

'. . . and, once you've taken on temporary British citizenship, I think this silly Land-Rover fuss will die down . . .'

A BOOK by novelist Penelope Mortimer, to be published this week, makes amazing allegations about the romantic life of the Queen Mother before her marriage.

MARCH 11

'I'm sorry. The Queen Mother is not to be disturbed — she's writing a torrid novel on the Life and Loves of Penelope Mortimer.'

'With so many sick people around, Mummy — why are they putting up prescription charges?'

MARCH 17

'I know we haven't officially started flogging off British Airways yet — but their offer for the stewardesses was irresistible!'

PRINCE ANDREW and Sarah Ferguson are engaged. Members of the Royal Family were told at the weekend to expect an 'imminent announcement'. It is believed that the Queen will make an official statement

MARCH 18

'I'm sorry, Andrew, but when I make the announcement, it'll be in the normal way!'

MARCH 19

'So much for your making a killing by hoarding spirits — now what're you going to do with the stuff?'

'I think I preferred the old tiger ads ...'

'Have yez heard the latest thick Scotland Yard man joke?'

'Isn't that nice, Sidney? This gentleman is so worried about flood damage at the Victoria and Albert Museum, he has volunteered to store a few treasures in his attic.'

mac

STOCKS AND SHARES

Maggie in firing line over shares

By GORDON GREIG
Political Editor

MRS THATCHER faces a stormy Commons inquisition today over her shares in an Australian company.

MARCH 26

'I'm afraid Mrs Thatcher's stock is at an all-time low.'

'They were so busy looking for drugs, they didn't notice me smuggling Scotch — want some ice with it?'

'It's Reagan about your latest suggestion of a John Lennon-type peace love-in, comrade Gorbachev . . .'

'Bedtime, Ian — it's net practice in the morning.'

'I wonder if that young jockey Richard Dunwoody who won the National is any relation of Gwyneth's . . . ?'

'It all started with Norman Fowler selling off the nurses' homes, then he sold the hospitals, then he . . .'

'So . . . all those in favour of Mayor Ramsbottom's proposal to update the Mayoral image . . . ?'

'. . . So, as usual, Andy my love, to save us any embarrassment in 50 years' time,
please swallow this letter after reading . . . Love Fergie xxx.'

'Okay, now that H.R.H. has made us aware of the mirror in our souls reflecting the beauty
and harmony of the universe — get those ✱✱✱✱✱✱✱ trees down!'

MINERS' leader Arthur Scargill lost his damages claim against South Yorkshire police yesterday. Now he faces a bill for costs estimated at well over £100,000.

MAY 9

'No offence meant, but, honestly, I just don't think the world is ready for an "Arthur-Aid" concert yet . . .'

'Hardly any vandalism — isn't it nice to hear of a team that can lose graciously?'

'Just relax, I'm going to give you something for that throat — open wide!'

BRITISH Caledonian announced yesterday that it is to cut staff by 1,000 in the wake of a slump in transatlantic travel.

With many American holidaymakers too frightened of terrorism to leave home, the airline faces the loss of about 50,000 passengers this summer.

MAY 16

'Bravery? — Shucks, that's nothin'! We flew across the Atlantic yesterday.'

'The damned cheek of the man, implicating the clergy! Whoever can he mean?'

'Before we leave you on your desert island, Parky, you're allowed one luxury item apart from the Bible or Shakespeare . . .'

'. . . If you are prepared to waste your time catching thugs, only for some soft old judge to let them go
or reduce their sentences, apply within . . .'

'. . . so please give generously to help the thousands of pitiful wrecks lying helplessly around Britain suffering from exhaustion, ruptures and blistered feet . . .'

'Thank heavens! Looks like they're getting rid of the dirt and garbage around Stonehenge at last.'

JUNE 2

'Please, Doris! I promise I'll let you have the telly for the Royal Wedding — now where have you hidden it?'

'A toffee wrapper? I didn't know I'd dropped a toffee wrapper!'

'Be reasonable, darling — we don't want to jeopardise my career as an MP or be unfair to homosexuals.'

'Britain has accepted a place in our rocket into space — a Mr Bobby Robson, and they want him left there.'

KURT WALDHEIM yesterday won a clear victory in Austria's presidential election as voters disregarded allegations that he was involved in Nazi war crimes.

JUNE 10

'Congratulations, Herr Waldheim — I expect by now you are racking your brains trying to decide on a Cabinet . . . ?'

'Right, lads — does everyone know what to do if an Argie steps into the exclusion zone?'

JUNE 23

'Good morning, vicar! — Remember cutting your sermon short last night, rushing out shouting "It's kick-off time!" and slamming the door behind you?'

'I don't care what the Ministry of Agriculture says, the sheep haven't been the same since Chernobyl . . .'

'Moshe! Your instructions were to burn all obscene posters on site — not take them down and store them under your bed!'

'Okay, I've turned off the supply — give them 12 hours, then gently lift up their dust-sheets and break the news about Botham's outburst.'

'I believe each of them is expected to clean 3,400 miles of road in 3 days, 8 hours and 40 minutes.'

JULY 1

JULY 4

'Ah, Pilbeam — let Jimmy Young out and tell the fella to put on a record or two . . .'

'Look at it this way, Geoffrey — with nobody willing to talk to you, peace is what you're likely to get.'

'Inhuman swines! Nobody should have the right to take another's life!'

'All right, keep the stumps and bails where they are — but can we have our bowler Chetan Sharma back?'

JULY 11

'Gent wants the latest on Geoffrey Howe — is he the one with the long blond hair or the one with the frock?'

'The show must go on, MacPherson — if nobody turns up, you're running against Seb Coe in the 800 metres.'

'Well? — When are you going to complain to the management about this overbooking?'

'As a display of unity, how does Ma'am feel about getting dressed up and going out on the town with the Prime Minister ?'

DALEY THOMPSON risks disqualification from the Commonwealth Games this morning in a £2 million row over sponsorship.

Thompson, a teetotaller, inked over the name of games sponsors Guinness on the number on the front of his vest yesterday in a personal protest at the brewery giant's involvement.

JULY 29

'. . . and the winner of the decathlon gold medal is . . . hang on, somebody's spilt Guinness all over the name.'

'Do be quick, Mrs Whitehouse. What's your complaint? We've got a board meeting going on!'

'Before we start, would anyone like a demonstration of the Anglo-American defence tactics used when an opponent comes at you with a sanctions demand?'

POLICE were last night preparing to interview Rolling Stones guitarist Bill Wyman following extraordinary claims that he took a 13-year-old girl as his mistress.

AUGUST 5

'It's the Rolling Stones' guitarist — he wants something fast and flashy to take his latest girlfriend out in'